Weight Watchers™

1 2 3 SUCCESS™

The Programme Cookbook
Roz Denny

SIMON & SCHUSTER
A VIACOM COMPANY

First published in Great Britain by Simon & Schuster, 1996
A Viacom Company

Copyright © 1996, Weight Watchers (UK) Ltd

Simon & Schuster Ltd
West Garden Place
Kendal Street
London W2 2AQ

Design: Green Moore Lowenhoff
Typesetting: Stylize
Photography: Iain Bagwell
Styling: Clare Hunt
Food preparation: Carol Tennant

Weight Watchers Publications Executive: Juliet Hudson
Weight Watchers Publications Assistant: Celia Whiston

ISBN 0-68481-800-0

Printed and bound in Italy by Rotolito Lombarda S.p.A.

Pictured on the front cover: *Chilli Chicken Salad (page 34) and
Quick Fish Crumble (page 56)*

Pictured on the back cover: *Berry Jelly Loaf and Plum and Mango Charlotte (page 70)*

Recipe notes:
Egg size is medium, unless otherwise stated.
Vegetables are medium-sized, unless otherwise stated.
The Points and Calorie values are for the main recipes only; remember to add extra
Points or Calories for the accompaniments.
It is important to use proper measuring spoons, not cutlery, for spoon measures.
1 tablespoon = 15 ml; 1 teaspoon = 5 ml.
Dried herbs can be substituted for fresh ones, but the flavour may not always
be as good. Halve the fresh-herb quantity stated in the recipe.

Vegetarian recipes:

V shows the recipe is vegetarian.

Contents

Introduction   4

Breakfasts   6

Snacks and Packed Lunches   10

Sandwiches and Rolls   20

Light Meals   26

Main Meals   44

Desserts   66

Index   80

Introduction

Welcome to *1,2,3 Success*™! – the cookbook that accompanies the brand new Weight Watchers Programme.

A quick flick through the scrumptious recipes that you'll find here will prove that 1,2,3 Success™ is something entirely different. Turkey Burgers on a diet? A B.L.T. sandwich? Sure, why not? Because with 1,2,3 Success™ you eat the food you like, when you like, and you fit it into a simple-to-manage eating plan.

Nothing in *1,2,3 Success*™: *The Programme Cookbook* is going to make you think, 'diet food again!'. Weight Watchers know that you can't stick to a diet if you don't like what you're eating – that's why we put together recipe collections like this one with real food, full of flavour and very satisfying (we've never believed in letting people go hungry). There's no problem getting anyone, whether they're dieting or not, to enjoy dishes as great as Barbecue Chicken Drumsticks or Rhubarb and Banana Fool with grated chocolate on top. So you don't have to prepare one thing for yourself and another for the family. You'll also find all the recipes in this book really easy to prepare.

Following the 1,2,3 Success™ Programme is simplicity itself. Every food is valued at a certain number of Points. Once you know how many Points you have to spend a day (your Weight Watchers Leader can tell you this) then you can plan each day as it comes.

With 1,2,3 Success™ you don't have to worry about whether your diet is healthy – foods with a lot of saturated fat have more Points, so you'll want to cut down on them to get the most from your daily Points allowance. You'll soon find yourself making healthy choices as a matter of course.

You'll be able to fill up on foods like bread, rice, pasta and potatoes which have only two or three Points per portion. These foods provide starch to give you energy and stop you feeling hungry. Choose wholemeal pasta or bread, brown rice, or potatoes with their skins on and they'll also provide the fibre you need in your diet.

Fruit and vegetables are also important for supplying fibre and for vitamins and minerals. Most fruits are only a half or one Point per portion and most vegetables have no Points at all, so you'll be able to eat plenty – Weight Watchers recommend five portions a day. This can easily fit into a day's eating – fruit juice or some banana cut up into your cereal for breakfast, a piece of fruit for a snack, a salad for lunch and two portions of lightly cooked vegetables with your supper – it soon adds up.

In *1,2,3 Success™: The Programme Cookbook* Points are given for both the whole recipe and for one serving. There are lots of serving suggestions too – do make sure, however, to include the extra Points. With 1,2,3 Success™ you can design your own diet and still lose weight. So start cooking Weight Watchers style and you'll soon be on the road to success.

Breakfasts

Always eat breakfast – even if you have it on the run. Otherwise your energy level may drop by mid-morning and you'll be more susceptible to bingeing on an unhealthy snack. These breakfast recipes are all fast and healthy.

Orange, Grapefruit and Kiwi Salad

Serves 2

Preparation time: 5 minutes
+ chilling
Calories per serving: 120

Freezing not recommended

This is a refreshing 'wake up' bowl of prepared fruits. Choose one of the sweeter grapefruits, such as pink or Sweetie.

1 large orange
1 sweet grapefruit
1 kiwi
a small handful of seedless
　green grapes
artificial sweetener (optional)
a good pinch of dried mint
　(optional)

1. Cut the tops and bottoms off the orange and grapefruit, and then stand the fruits upright on a board and, using a small sharp knife, cut away the peel and white pith in strips.
2. Peel the kiwi and remove the core at the top of the fruit. Slice the citrus fruits and kiwi, saving any juices. Halve the grapes.
3. Divide the fruits between two bowls, and then sprinkle with the sweetener and mint, if using. Chill for an hour or so before serving.

Per serving: **P 2**
Total per recipe: **P 4**

Tomatoes on Pesto Toast

Serves 1

Preparation and cooking time: 5 minutes
Calories per serving: 220

Freezing not recommended

This old fashioned favourite is given a modern Mediterranean twist with a little pesto sauce. Use a full-flavoured and ripe tomato.

1 teaspoon sunflower
　margarine
2 teaspoons pesto sauce
1 large ripe tomato
1 slice of wholemeal or Granary
　bread
salt and freshly ground black
　pepper

1. Preheat the grill. Mix together the margarine and pesto sauce.
2. Halve the tomato widthways and season well. Grill for 3 minutes on the cut side only, until lightly browned.
3. Meanwhile, lightly toast the bread on both sides.
4. Spread half the pesto mix on the toast, top with the tomato halves and divide the remaining pesto mix between the tomatoes, spreading carefully with a knife. Scatter with freshly ground black pepper and serve.

Per serving: **P 2½**

Scrambled Egg and Soy Mushrooms

Serves 2

Preparation and cooking time: 7 minutes
Calories per serving: 160

Freezing not recommended

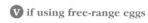 if using free-range eggs

120 g (4 oz) button mushrooms
1 tablespoon sunflower oil
2 tablespoons light soy sauce
2 eggs, beaten
¹/₂ punnet of salad cress, snipped
freshly ground black pepper

Creamy scrambled eggs are always popular. These have a tasty addition and are excellent for brunch or a weekend breakfast. Serve with sesame-seed rye crispbread.

1. Halve the mushrooms if large. Heat the oil in a small non-stick saucepan and quickly fry the mushrooms, stirring and tossing for about 2 minutes.
2. Mix in the soy sauce and season with black pepper. Cook for another minute or so, then remove with a slotted spoon.
3. Wipe out the pan with kitchen paper and return to the heat until hot. Lightly coat the base with some low-fat cooking spray.
4. Season the eggs with pepper only and, when the pan is hot, stir in the eggs.
5. Scramble until lightly set and then mix in the mushrooms. Serve immediately, topped with snipped cress.

Per serving: P 3
Total per recipe: P 6

Yogurt, Banana and Strawberry Refresher

Serves 1

Preparation time: 3 minutes
Calories per serving: 250

Freezing not recommended

1 tablespoon porridge oats
150 g (5 oz) low-fat natural yogurt
2 teaspoons clear honey
1 small ripe banana
3 ripe strawberries
a good pinch of cinnamon

This fruit smoothie is full of energy, very satisfying – and tastes great too. You can use a handful of fresh raspberries instead of the strawberries, if you prefer.

1. Heat a small, non-stick frying-pan until really hot, and then dry-fry the oats for about 2 minutes until lightly toasted, stirring occasionally. Allow to cool. (If you intend to make this dish frequently it might be worth toasting more oats at a time.)
2. Mix the yogurt with the honey and spoon into a pretty glass dish.
3. Slice the banana on top of the yogurt. Hull the strawberries and slice them on top of the banana.
4. Scatter with the cinnamon and toasted oats before serving.

Per serving: P 4¹/₂

Snacks and Packed Lunches

Increasingly, nowadays, it seems that we eat at least one meal in the day away from home. Meals in cafés, canteens and pubs tend to be high in Points and Calories – which can make life difficult for those of us trying to lose weight. There are also times when you want just 'a little something' to keep hunger pangs at bay and prevent yourself from reaching for the biscuit packet. With 1,2,3 Success you can fit small meals and snacks into your day. Simply add on the Points as you go.

To bridge that hunger gap, here are some simple packed meals and quick fillers that are healthy, low in Points and Calories, and easy to put together. And they taste good enough to enable you to resist the urge to order a high-Calorie take-away.

If you can, do try to get your packed lunch ready the night before, and store it in an air-tight container. Don't forget cutlery and a paper napkin. Include some raw, crisp vegetables and one or two good pieces of fresh fruit plus some mineral water or a low-Calorie drink. These will help fill you up without using up your Points.

Mexican Tomato Salsa

Serves 4

Preparation time: 12 minutes
Calories per serving: 35

Freezing not recommended

Serve this as a lovely fresh dip with crudités or tortilla chips. This salsa can also be served as a delicious sauce with grilled fish or chicken. Simply spoon over. Best of all it has no Points!

4 ripe tomatoes
1 small green chilli or 1
   teaspoon mild chilli powder
1 small red pepper, de-seeded
   and chopped roughly
1/2 small onion, chopped
   roughly
1 small garlic clove, crushed
juice of 1 lime or 1/2 lemon
2 tablespoons chopped fresh
   coriander or parsley
salt and freshly ground black
   pepper

1. Score the base of each tomato with a sharp knife, just to break the skin. Place in a large bowl and cover with boiling water.
2. Leave for a minute, then drain and run under cold water. Peel off the skins and quarter the tomatoes.
3. Cut out the cores and chop the flesh finely. Season and set aside.
4. Slit the chilli lengthways, if using, and scoop out the seeds. Chop roughly. Take care: fresh chilli juice can sting if you touch your eyes.
5. Put the pepper, onion, chilli and garlic into a food processor or blender and process into a chunky purée.
6. Mix into the chopped tomato. Add the lime or lemon juice, chopped herbs and plenty of seasoning, including the chilli powder, if using.
7. Spoon into a serving bowl, cover and chill for at least an hour before serving.

Per serving: **P 0**
Total per recipe: **P 0**

Tomato, Orange and Olive Salad

Serves 4

Preparation time: 12 minutes
Calories per serving: 50

Freezing not recommended

This salad has a lovely sunny Mediterranean feel. Try it with cold, cooked chicken, sliced lean ham or wafer-thin slices of low-fat cheese.

1 large orange
4 tomatoes, quartered and cut
    into chunks
1/2 small red onion, sliced thinly
60 g (2 oz) fresh baby leaf
    spinach or Cos lettuce,
    shredded
2 tablespoons stoned black
    olives, sliced
2 tablespoons low-fat french
    dressing
salt and freshly ground black
    pepper

1. Cut both ends off the orange and stand upright on a board. Using a small sharp knife, slice the peel and membrane away in strips. Cut into chunks the same size as the tomatoes.
2. Mix with the rest of the ingredients, season well and chill lightly before serving.

Per serving: **P** 1/2
Total per recipe: **P** 2

Felafels

Makes 8

Preparation time: 15 minutes
+ chilling
Cooking time: 20 minutes
Calories per felafel: 60

Freezing recommended

Felafels are chick-pea patties; they are popular street food in the Middle East. Serve tucked into mini pitta breads with some sliced lettuce, tomato and cucumber. You could, if you like, serve simply with a green leaf salad and top with a little

natural yogurt or sprinkle with fresh lemon juice, for a really delicious, satisfying snack.

420 g (14 oz) canned chick-
    peas, drained
1 garlic clove, crushed
1–2 tablespoons plain flour
1 teaspoon ground coriander
1/2 teaspoon ground cumin
1 teaspoon salt
2 tablespoons chopped fresh
    parsley
1 tablespoon olive or sunflower
    oil
freshly ground black pepper

1. Pat the chick-peas dry with some kitchen paper.
2. Place in a food processor with the garlic, flour, spices, salt and pepper. Blend to a thick purée that you can shape into patties. If the mixture looks a little runny, add a spoonful more flour and blend again.
3. Scoop into a bowl and mix in the parsley. Divide the mixture into eight. Dip your hands in cold water and shape the mixture into eight balls. Slightly flatten each one. Chill for about an hour in the fridge.
4. Preheat the oven to Gas Mark 5/190°C/375°F. Place the patties on a non-stick baking tray and brush the tops lightly with the oil. Bake for about 20 minutes, until golden brown.

Per serving: **P** 1
Total per recipe: **P** 8

Red Bean Dip

Serves 6

Preparation time: 10 minutes
Calories per serving: 85

Freezing not recommended

Serve with bread sticks or fingers of raw vegetables, such as cucumber, carrot, peppers and celery, for a tasty low-Point snack.

420 g (14 oz) canned red
   kidney beans, drained and
   rinsed
1–2 garlic cloves, crushed
1 teaspoon ground coriander
$\frac{1}{2}$ teaspoon ground cumin
2 tablespoons olive oil
juice of 1 lemon
salt and freshly ground black
   pepper
chopped fresh parsley, to serve
   (optional)

1. Mash the beans well with a fork, or blend in a food processor. Mix in the remaining ingredients.
2. Spoon into a plastic food container or dish. Chill until ready to serve.

Per serving: **P** **1½**
Total per recipe: **P** **9**

Trio of Grated Salads

Serves 4

Preparation time: 15 minutes
Calories per serving:
carrot salad 50;
cucumber salad 20;
beetroot and apple salad 50
Freezing not recommended

None of these salads takes long to prepare and the flavours complement each other wonderfully. However, if you do fancy one on its own, see below for the individual Points total.

For the carrot salad:
3 carrots
2 teaspoons olive oil
juice of 1 small lemon
2 tablespoons chopped fresh
   mint or parsley
salt and freshly ground black
   pepper

Per serving: **P** **½**
Total per recipe: **P** **2**

For the cucumber salad:
1 whole cucumber
2 salad onions, chopped finely
3 tablespoons low-fat bio
   natural yogurt
1 teaspoon dried dill
salt and freshly ground black
   pepper

Per serving: **P** **0**
Total per recipe: **P** **0**

For the beetroot and apple salad:
2 whole pickled beetroot
1 large dessert apple
2 teaspoons olive oil
1 tablespoon wine vinegar, red
   or white
a good pinch of cumin seeds
   (optional)
salt and freshly ground black
   pepper

Per serving: **P** **½**
Total per recipe: **P** **2**

1. Grate the carrots coarsely and mix with the oil, lemon juice, herbs and seasoning.
2. Halve the cucumber lengthways, scoop out the seeds with a teaspoon and coarsely grate the flesh. Season lightly and mix with the chopped onions, yogurt and dill.
3. Drain the beetroot and pat dry with kitchen paper. Core and quarter the apple. Grate both coarsely and mix with the oil, vinegar, cumin, if using, and seasoning.
4. Put the salads in separate serving dishes or food containers and chill lightly before serving.

Barbecue Chicken Drumsticks

Serves 4

Preparation and cooking time: 15–20 minutes + marinating
Calories per serving: 150

Freezing not recommended

These are excellent hot or cold and are ideal finger food for lunch boxes. If serving them at home as a light meal, add some salad and crusty bread, or hot boiled rice.

8 chicken drumsticks
2 tablespoons dark soy sauce
1 tablespoon dry sherry
1 teaspoon clear honey
1 garlic clove, crushed
1 tablespoon grated fresh root ginger or ginger paste
1 teaspoon ground coriander
1/2 teaspoon ground cinnamon
freshly ground black pepper

1. Skin the drumsticks. Mix the remaining ingredients and pour into a plastic food bag.
2. Add the drumsticks, rub everything together well, seal the bag and marinate for 2 hours.
3. When ready to cook, preheat the grill until glowing and then turn down to a medium heat.
4. Drain the drumsticks and grill for about 6 minutes on each side or until cooked through.

Cook's note:
Root ginger keeps very well in the fridge or freezer and can be grated from frozen.

Per serving: **P 2½**
Total per recipe: **P 10**

Pepper Omelette

Serves 4

Preparation time: 12 minutes
Calories per serving: 160

Freezing not recommended

V if using free-range eggs

A great use for cold cooked potato! This makes an excellent picnic or packed lunch dish; serve it cold in wedges. It's good with sliced tomatoes and cucumber.

1 tablespoon olive oil
1 green pepper, sliced thinly
1 red or yellow pepper, sliced thinly
1 onion, sliced thinly
2 garlic clove, crushed
1 potato, cooked and sliced thinly
1/2 teaspoon mild chilli powder (optional)
4 eggs
1 teaspoon dried oregano or mixed herbs
salt and freshly ground black pepper

1. Heat a medium-sized, non-stick frying-pan until hot. Add the oil and swirl around to coat.
2. Add the peppers, onion and garlic, stir well, then cover and cook over a gentle heat for 5 minutes, until softened.
3. Stir in the potato and chilli powder, if using, and cook for another 5 minutes.
4. Beat the eggs with the herbs and seasoning, and pour into the pan, stirring lightly to mix everything together. Preheat the grill.
5. Cook over a gentle heat for about 12–15 minutes, without stirring again, until firmly set.
6. Put the frying-pan under the grill and brown the top of the omelette for the last 2 minutes of cooking.
7. Leave the omelette to stand for 5 minutes, before loosening the sides and shaking out on to a board or plate. Allow to cool before cutting into wedges.

Per serving: **P 2½**
Total per recipe: **P 10**

Brown Rice and Bean Salad

Serves 4

Preparation time: 15 minutes
+ cooling
Cooking time: 20–25 minutes
Calories per serving: 230

Freezing not recommended

Ⓥ if using vegetarian cheese

**Beans and rice are a perfect
nutritionally balanced meal,
which is also low in fat.
Ideally, use brown basmati
rice for this salad; it has a
wonderfully aromatic
flavour, and takes less time
to cook than other brown
rices.**

150 g (5 oz) brown rice (ideally:
  brown basmati)
1 teaspoon mild curry powder
3 tablespoons low-Calorie
  french dressing
1 small red onion, sliced thinly
1 small yellow or green pepper,
  sliced thinly
1 celery stick, sliced thinly
210 g (7 oz) canned kidney
  beans or butter beans,
  drained and rinsed
60 g (2 oz) low-fat Cheddar
  cheese, cut in small cubes
a bunch of watercress, stalks
  removed
salt and freshly ground black
  pepper

1. Boil the rice according to the packet instructions. Drain and
rinse in cold water. Mix the curry powder with the dressing and,
before the rice cools completely, toss it in the dressing. Season well
and leave until cold, stirring occasionally.
2. Toss with the vegetables, beans and cheese cubes. Carefully mix
in the watercress. Check the seasoning and serve.

Per serving: **P** 3½
Total per recipe: **P** 14

Mackerel and Macaroni Salad

Serves 4

**Preparation and cooking
time:** 20 minutes + cooling
Calories per serving: 240

Freezing not recommended

**This is a nice all-in-one lunch
box salad. Smoked mackerel
is a very healthy fish that is
high in omega-3 fatty acids,
which help to protect against
heart disease.**

150 g (5 oz) macaroni
2 tablespoons low-Calorie
  french dressing
120 g (4 oz) smoked mackerel
  fillets, skinned
2 salad onions, chopped
6 cherry tomatoes, halved
1 carrot, grated coarsely
3 tablespoons low-fat bio
  natural yogurt
1 punnet of salad cress
salt and freshly ground black
  pepper

1. Boil the macaroni according to the packet instructions. Drain
and toss in the dressing. Leave to cool.
2. Flake the fish, taking care to remove any stray bones.
3. When the pasta is cold, mix it with the fish. Add the salad onions,
tomatoes, carrot and yogurt.
4. Mix half of the cress into the salad. Season to taste.
5. Spoon the salad into a bowl and scatter over the remaining cress.

Variation:
Use 150 g (5 oz) of canned tuna in brine instead of the mackerel.
Drain it well. This will be 2 Points per serving and the total Points
per recipe will be 8 (200 Calories per serving).

Per serving: **P** 4
Total per recipe: **P** 16

Sandwiches and Rolls

If you use really good, very fresh bread for sandwiches you'll find it's so flavourful that you won't need to use any butter or margarine, which will help save Points. Pitta breads make good sandwiches, too. Allow one mini pitta or half a normal-sized one per serving – and, again, make sure they are really fresh.

Use lettuce leaves, sliced tomato and cucumber in your sandwiches; these have no Points but add moisture and 'crunch'. If you like crisps, allow yourself the occasional treat of a few low-fat crisps, by placing three or four inside the sandwich with the filling just before you bite into it for a crisp 'butty'. Wrapping sandwiches well in clingfilm will help prevent them from drying out – even if you are putting them into a sandwich box.

Tuna and Onion Sandwiches

Serves 2

Preparation time: 5 minutes
Calories per serving: 230

Freezing not recommended

100 g can of tuna in brine, drained
3 tablespoons Quark or semi-skimmed soft cheese
1 salad onion, chopped finely
4 slices of wholemeal bread
1 tablespoon low-fat spread
salt and freshly ground black pepper

1. Flake the tuna finely and blend with the Quark, onion and seasoning until smooth.
2. 'Butter' the bread with the low-fat spread, divide the tuna between 2 slices, and top with the remaining bread. Cut each sandwich in half and wrap in clingfilm until required.

Per serving: **P** **4**
Total per recipe: **P** **8**

Classic B.L.T.

Serves 1

Preparation and cooking time: 10 minutes
Calories per serving: 230

Freezing not recommended

1 lean rasher of back bacon (ideally smoked)
1 ripe tomato, sliced
2 lettuce leaves, shredded
2 slices of wholemeal or Granary bread, toasted, or a split roll
1 teaspoon low-Calorie mayonnaise

1. Trim the bacon of any fat. Heat a small non-stick frying-pan until hot then flash-fry the rasher on both sides until just cooked – this will take about 2 minutes.
2. Place the tomato and lettuce on one slice of toast or in a split roll. Top with the bacon.
3. Spread the mayonnaise on the other slice of toast or roll and press down.

Per serving: **P** **5**

Salmon Sandwiches with Lemon and Cucumber

Serves 2

Preparation time: 5 minutes
Calories per serving: 265

Freezing not recommended

210 g (7 oz) canned pink or red salmon, drained
2 teaspoons low-Calorie mayonnaise
1 teaspoon horseradish sauce or relish
1 teaspoon grated lemon zest
a squeeze of fresh lemon juice
6 slices of cucumber
1 small salad onion, chopped
4 slices of bread or 2 split rolls
salt and freshly ground black pepper

1. Flake the fish finely, including the soft bones as these are a good source of calcium.
2. Mix with the mayonnaise, horseradish, lemon zest and juice. Season well.
3. Stack the cucumber slices on top of each other and cut into shreds. Mix these into the salmon with the onion and divide between the bread or split rolls.

Per serving: **P 5**
Total per recipe: **P 10**

Scrambled Egg and Sesame Pitta

Serves 1

Preparation and cooking time: 5 minutes
Calories per serving: 260

Freezing not recommended

Ⓥ

1 egg
1 teaspoon light soy sauce
1 teaspoon sunflower oil
½ teaspoon sesame oil
1 teaspoon sesame seeds
1 mini pitta, halved
1–2 tablespoons snipped salad cress
salt and freshly ground black pepper

1. Beat the egg, soy sauce and a little seasoning.
2. Heat the sunflower oil in a small non-stick pan and, when hot, lightly scramble the egg. Remove the pan from the heat when the egg is lightly set and mix in the sesame oil and seeds.
3. Open up the pitta halves and divide the egg between them. Stuff in the cress and serve at once.

Per serving:  **P 5½**

Prawn Bap

Serves 1

Preparation time: 5 minutes
+ thawing
Calories per serving: 225

Freezing not recommended

For the best flavour, use
North Atlantic cold water
prawns, which are readily
available in supermarkets,
and buy a freshly baked bap
so you won't need to butter
it! This is a substantial snack
and you may need to eat it
with a knife and fork!

60 g (2 oz) peeled prawns,
    thawed if frozen
juice of $\frac{1}{2}$ lemon
1 bap
2 lettuce leaves
1 tomato, sliced
6 thin slices of cucumber
2 teaspoons low-Calorie
    mayonnaise
1 small salad onion, chopped
a good pinch of paprika
salt and freshly ground black
    pepper

1. Sprinkle the prawns with the lemon juice and some black
pepper. (If they are frozen this can be done as they thaw. Pat dry
with kitchen paper if they are wet.)
2. Split the bap in half and place a lettuce leaf on each half. Arrange
the tomato and cucumber slices on top, and then spoon on the
prawns. Season lightly.
3. Put the mayonnaise on top of that and sprinkle with the chopped
onion and paprika. Eat as soon as possible.

Variation:
Use 2 thin slices of very lean ham, first removing any fat; this will be
$5\frac{1}{2}$ Points per serving.

Per serving: **P 6**

Mango Curry Chicken Rolls

Serves 2

**Preparation and cooking
time:** 20 minutes
Calories per serving: 315

Freezing not recommended

These summery salad baps
contain cold, cooked chicken
in a light Coronation-style
sauce. Serve with some
whole radishes.

150 g (5 oz) cooked, skinned
    chicken, shredded thinly
$\frac{1}{2}$ small celery stick, sliced
    thinly
1 small carrot, grated coarsely
1 tablespoon lemon juice
1 tablespoon chopped fresh
    parsley
2 baps
2 teaspoons low-fat spread
2 crisp lettuce leaves
1 tomato, sliced thinly
For the sauce:
1 small salad onion, chopped
1 teaspoon mild curry powder
2 teaspoons mango chutney
2 tablespoons low-fat natural
    yogurt
salt and freshly ground black
    pepper

1. Mix together the shredded chicken with the celery, carrot, lemon
juice, parsley and seasoning.
2. Mix together the sauce ingredients and fold into the chicken.
3. Halve the baps and spread with the low-fat spread. Divide the
filling between the two baps, top with lettuce and tomato slices,
and sandwich together. Wrap in clingfilm until required.

Per serving: **P 8½**
Total per recipe: **P 17**

Light Meals

'Little and often' is sometimes recommended if you are trying hard to re-establish good eating habits. If you tend to eat one heavy meal a day, try switching to two lighter ones – this has the bonus of giving you another meal to look forward to.

Included in this chapter are a selection of light meals which satisfy your hunger without leaving you feeling that you can't move. Home-made soup is always a good meal in itself. The hot, delicious liquid fills you up and it's cheap and quick to prepare. Eggs are a good starting point for light meals – they're nature's convenience food, all neatly packaged and easy to crack open, ready to produce a good meal within minutes. I've also included some light meals based on rice, pasta, bread and potatoes – these will not only satisfy you but will provide you with lots of energy.

Finally, for one of the freshest, lightest meals around, nothing beats a large plate or bowl of fresh vegetables – it's amazing how satisfying a large portion can be. Add a little low-Calorie dressing or sauce and the result will still be low in Points.

Smooth Broccoli Soup with Garlic Cheese Clouds

Serves 4

Preparation and cooking time: 20 minutes
Calories per serving: 100

Freezing recommended, without the cheese clouds

This couldn't be simpler and the flavour is so fresh. You will need a food processor to purée the broth and florets very thoroughly.

960 g (2 lb) broccoli heads
2 teaspoons salt
105 g (3½ oz) Quark or skimmed milk soft cheese
1–2 tablespoons skimmed milk
1 small garlic clove, crushed
2 teaspoons chopped fresh herbs
freshly ground black pepper

1. Trim the broccoli of stalks until you have short florets, about 390 g (13 oz) in weight.
2. Put the salt and 750 ml (1¼ pints) water into a large saucepan, bring to the boil and add the florets. Return to the boil and simmer for 10 minutes.
3. Remove the florets from the pan with a slotted spoon and put in a food processor with a little cooking water. Do not throw any of the water away!
4. Blend the florets until very, very smooth and silky. This will take 2–3 minutes. The texture will become like soft, runny butter and the colour will be bright green. You will need to scrape the sides of the machine down between processing.
5. With the machine running, gradually pour in the remaining broccoli water. Strain the soup back into the saucepan through a sieve. Season with some pepper.
6. To make the cheese clouds, beat the Quark with the skimmed milk until you have a soft, dropping texture. Mix in the crushed garlic and herbs.
7. Reheat the soup and pour into four warmed bowls. Drop small dollops of cheese mixture to float on top of the soup and serve at once. Sprinkle with a little more chopped herbs, if you like.

Per serving: **P** ½
Total per recipe: **P** 2

Chunky Bortsch

Serves 4

Preparation time: 10 minutes
Cooking time: 30 minutes
Calories per serving: 115

Freezing recommended

This is a beautifully coloured, warming soup that fills you up, but is very healthy and low in Calories. It's good with a chunk of crusty bread or some light rye crackers.

1 onion, chopped finely
360 g (12 oz) raw beetroot, peeled and chopped finely
1 medium cooking apple, cored and chopped finely
1 celery stick, sliced finely
1/2 red pepper, chopped finely
75 g (2 1/2 oz) button mushrooms, sliced finely
4 teaspoons sunflower oil
1 litre (1 3/4 pints) water
1 teaspoon ground cumin
2 teaspoons ground coriander
a good pinch of dried thyme
a large bay leaf
salt and freshly ground black pepper
4 tablespoons low-fat bio natural yogurt, to serve

1. Put all the vegetables into a large saucepan with the oil and 3 tablespoons of water. Stir well and heat until the vegetables start sizzling.
2. Cover with a well-fitting lid and turn the heat right down. Sweat the vegetables for about 10 minutes, shaking the pan occasionally.
3. Add the water, cumin, coriander and herbs. Season well, bring to the boil and simmer, uncovered, for 15 minutes, until the vegetables are soft. Remove the bay leaf.
4. Ladle into four warmed soup bowls and top with the yogurt.

Per serving: **P 1**
Total per recipe: **P 4**

Summer Salad Bowl with Green Yogurt Dressing

Serves 2

Preparation time: 10 minutes
Calories per serving: 125

Freezing not recommended

This is a warm-weather version of the steamed vegetable dish on page 31; it's a bowl of deliciously crisp and colourful salad vegetables served with a fresh herb dressing that's creamy but low in Points. Mooli, or daikon radish, is a large, white, mild radish from Japan. Thinly sliced or shredded, it makes a delicious addition to any mixed salad.

1/4 cucumber
2 Little Gem lettuces, sliced
1 carrot, grated coarsely
3 salad onions, sliced
1 small green or yellow pepper, sliced thinly
2 celery sticks or 1/2 fennel bulb, sliced thinly
1 bag of rocket leaves or half a bunch of watercress, trimmed
1/4 mooli or daikon radish, sliced thinly (optional)
For the dressing:
150 g (5 oz) low-fat bio natural yogurt
1 tablespoon chopped fresh chives or salad onion tops
3 tablespoons chopped fresh parsley
1 tablespoon chopped fresh dill, or 1 teaspoon dried
1 tablespoon chopped fresh mint
salt and freshly ground black pepper

1. Halve the cucumber lengthways and scoop out the seeds with a teaspoon. Slice the two halves thinly on a diagonal.
2. Mix all the salad vegetables together in a big bowl and season well.
3. Mix the dressing ingredients together, adding a little water if you want a thinner dressing. Trickle over the salad and toss well.

Per serving: **P 1**
Total per recipe: **P 2**

Devilled Mushrooms on Toast

Serves 2

Preparation and cooking time: 10 minutes
Calories per serving: 125

Freezing not recommended

This is a much lighter version of a traditional supper favourite; I've left out the cream but it's just as delicious.

3 teaspoons low-fat spread
210 g (7 oz) button
  mushrooms, halved if large
1–2 teaspoons coarse-grained
  mustard
2 teaspoons Worcestershire
  sauce
1 tablespoon low-fat soft cheese
1 salad onion, chopped finely,
  or 1 tablespoon chopped
  fresh chives
2 slices of wholemeal bread
salt and freshly ground black
  pepper

1. In a saucepan, melt 1 teaspoon of the spread with 2 tablespoons of water. Stir in the mushrooms. Season well and cover; turn the heat down to a simmer.
2. Cook for 5 minutes, stirring occasionally. Uncover and mix in the mustard, Worcestershire sauce and soft cheese. Stir everything together well and mix in the onion or chives.
3. Meanwhile, lightly toast the bread and spread with the remaining low-fat spread. Pile the mushrooms on top and serve immediately.

Per serving: P 2
Total per recipe: P 4

Steamed Vegetable Platter

Serves 2

Preparation and cooking time: 20 minutes
Calories per serving: 240

Freezing not recommended

When you feel like giving your system a good inner cleanse, a plate heaped with freshly steamed vegetables tossed with a light oriental dressing is just the job. It's also a good way to fill up using minimum Points. You can use whatever vegetables you like or are available. A steamer is a useful kitchen tool to have around – steaming is a very healthy way to cook. If you don't have a steamer, see if you have a metal colander that will fit inside a large saucepan (without touching the bottom!). You'll also need a lid for the saucepan.

1 carrot, cut in thin sticks
1 turnip, cut in thin sticks
60 g (2 oz) baby sweetcorn
1 courgette, cut in thick slices
60 g (2 oz) whole green beans
  or mange-tout, trimmed
1 leek, sliced
¼ cauliflower, cut in florets
1 head of broccoli, cut in florets
1 punnet of salad cress,
  snipped
salt and freshly ground black
  pepper
For the dressing:
3 tablespoons light soy sauce
1 tablespoon olive or sunflower
  oil
1 teaspoon sesame oil
1 tablespoon white wine
  vinegar
1 teaspoon clear honey

1. Fill the steamer with water and put it on to boil. When the water boils, put the carrot, turnip and sweetcorn in the steamer basket. Steam the vegetables for 2 minutes.
2. Add the courgette, beans and leek and steam for another 2 minutes. Add the cauliflower and broccoli and continue steaming for a further 2–3 minutes, until the florets feel just tender but not soft.
3. While the vegetables are steaming, whisk the dressing ingredients together. Tip the steamed vegetables into a large serving bowl, season lightly, toss in the dressing and scatter over the snipped cress.

Per serving: P 2½
Total per recipe: P 5

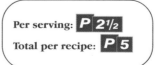

Baked Potatoes

Serves 2

Preparation time: 10–15 minutes
Cooking time: 10 minutes – 1 hour (depending on whether microwave is used)
Calories per serving: courgette and tomato filling 210; **sweet pepper and creamy red bean filling** 260; **cottage cheese and prawn filling** 215.

Freezing not recommended

 except for the cottage cheese and prawn filling

Baked potatoes are the ideal quick, light, tasty meal. Choose one of these fillings to stuff two potatoes.

2 × 150 g (5 oz) potatoes
salt and freshly ground black pepper

For the courgette and tomato filling:
1 courgette, sliced
1 small onion, sliced
2 teaspoons sunflower oil
210 g (7 oz) canned chopped tomatoes
a good pinch of mixed herbs
30 g (1 oz) low-fat Cheddar cheese, grated

Per serving: **P 3**
Total per recipe: **P 6**

For the sweet pepper and creamy red bean filling:
1 small red or yellow pepper, sliced thinly
1 small onion
2 teaspoons olive or sunflower oil
1/2 teaspoon paprika
a good pinch of dried thyme
a good pinch of ground cumin
210 g (7 oz) red kidney beans, drained
2 tablespoons low-fat soft cheese

Per serving: **P 3½**
Total per recipe: **P 7**

For the cottage cheese and prawn filling:
210 g (7 oz) low-fat cottage cheese
75 g (2½ oz) peeled prawns, thawed if frozen
1 salad onion, chopped
2 teaspoons light soy sauce
a little salad cress or chopped fresh parsley

Per serving: **P 3½**
Total per recipe: **P 7**

1. Score a big cross on the top of each potato and wash well, patting dry with kitchen paper.
2. To microwave: place on a sheet of kitchen paper and cook on full power (100%) according to your oven's instructions. To bake conventionally: preheat the oven to Gas Mark 6/200°C/400°F. Rub the potato skin with some sea salt to make the potato crisp on the outside and soft in the centre. Bake for 1 hour.
3. When cooked, let the potatoes stand for 3 minutes before cutting open along the scored lines and pushing up the base. Spoon in your favourite filling.
4. For the courgette and tomato filling, put the courgette and the onion in a saucepan and cook over a gentle heat for 5 minutes. Add the tomatoes and the herbs. Season and cook for 5 minutes more and serve with the cheese sprinkled on top.
5. For the sweet pepper and creamy red bean filling, put the pepper and onion in a saucepan with the oil and 2 tablespoons of water. Cook gently for 5 minutes, until softened. Add the paprika, thyme and cumin. Cook for a few seconds and then add the kidney beans. Reheat until very hot and then season well. Stir in the cheese.
6. For the cottage cheese and prawn filling, mix the cottage cheese with the prawns. Stir in the salad onion and soy sauce. Top with the snipped salad cress or parsley.

Chicken, Orange and Chinese Leaf Stir-fry

Serves 4

Preparation time: 12 minutes
Cooking time: 10 minutes
Calories per serving: 210

Freezing not recommended

Chinese leaf is a wonderfully versatile vegetable; it is lovely and crisp used raw in salads or it can be lightly cooked and served as a vegetable. It also keeps very well and will last a week or so in the fridge. This recipe is delicious with Chinese egg noodles.

1 tablespoon sunflower oil
390 g (13 oz) skinless, boneless chicken breast, sliced thinly
1 small red pepper, de-seeded and sliced thinly
3 salad onions, sliced
105 g (3½ oz) Chinese leaf, shredded
1 cm (½-inch) piece of fresh root ginger, grated
2 garlic cloves, crushed
1 teaspoon sesame seeds
For the sauce:
juice of 1 orange
4 tablespoons soy sauce
1 tablespoon dry sherry
1 teaspoon sesame oil
1 teaspoon cornflour
salt and freshly ground black pepper

1. Heat the oil in a non-stick wok until quite hot and quickly stir-fry the chicken for 2 minutes until browned.
2. Remove the meat with a wooden spoon and add the vegetables, ginger, garlic and 3 tablespoons of water. Stir-fry for 3 minutes, until the Chinese leaf starts to wilt.
3. Meanwhile, mix all the sauce ingredients together in a small jug, until smooth. Pour into the wok and mix until you have a smooth glossy sauce.
4. Return the chicken to the pan, check the seasoning and reheat for a minute or two. Scatter over the sesame seeds and serve immediately.

Per serving: **P 3½**
Total per recipe: **P 14**

Chilli Chicken Salad

Serves 2

Preparation time: 10 minutes
Calories per serving: 220

Freezing not recommended

This dish uses cooked chicken breasts, which you'll find readily available. Remove the skin because this is high in Calories and fat. Make sure you include some crunchy salad vegetables – I've used celery, pepper and apples, but you can use whatever you like best. This is excellent served with a couple of crispbreads.

2 × 75 g (2½ oz) cooked chicken breasts, skinned and shredded
2 celery sticks, sliced thinly, or ½ small fennel bulb, sliced thinly
½ small yellow or red pepper, sliced thinly
1 small Granny Smith apple, cored and sliced
2 salad onions, chopped
6 large radishes, sliced
105 g (3½ oz) Iceberg lettuce, shredded
3 tablespoons low-Calorie french dressing
1–2 tablespoons chilli relish or barbecue relish
salt and freshly ground black pepper

1. Put the chicken, celery, pepper, apple, onions, radishes and lettuce in a large bowl. Season well, and toss together.
2. Mix the dressing with the relish and toss with the salad. Serve immediately.

Per serving: **P 4**
Total per recipe: **P 8**

Turkey Burgers

Serves 4

Preparation time: 5 minutes
Cooking time: 10 minutes
Calories per serving: 130

Freezing not recommended

Turkey mince is very lean; it contains less than 5% fat and it's also very tasty. It makes delicious light and juicy burgers. Serve them with salad and either a small jacket potato or a mini pitta bread, or even clamped inside a small wholemeal burger bap!

480 g (1 lb) turkey mince
1 small onion, grated
1 teaspoon garlic salt
1 tablespoon Worcestershire sauce
1 tablespoon mild chilli relish
freshly ground black pepper

1. Preheat a non-stick frying-pan slowly to a steady medium heat.
2. Meanwhile, mix the mince with the onion, garlic salt, Worcestershire sauce and relish. Divide the mixture into four and shape into neat round patties, dipping your hands in cold water if the mixture sticks to them.
3. Use a low-fat spray to coat the frying-pan just before cooking. Add the burgers to the pan, flattening each slightly with a palette knife.
4. Cook over a medium heat for about 5 minutes on each side, until just firm. Do not overcook or the meat will become dry. Season again just before serving in the same way as traditional burgers.

Per serving: **P** **4**
Total per recipe: **P** **16**

Spinach Soufflé Omelette

Serves 1

Preparation and cooking time: 12 minutes
Calories per serving: 245

Freezing not recommended

 if using free-range eggs

Omelettes are not difficult to make and they're really satisfying; you feel you've had a proper meal. This soufflé omelette contains spinach and so is particularly nutritious. Have it with a few slices of tomato and a couple of rye crispbreads.

105 g (3½ oz) baby spinach leaves, washed and drained
2 teaspoons grated fresh parmesan cheese, or
1 tablespoon grated low-fat cheese
2 eggs, separated
½ teaspoon sunflower or olive oil
salt and freshly ground black pepper and freshly grated nutmeg

1. Cook the spinach without any additional water until just wilted – this will take about 2 minutes. Drain well, allow to cool and chop finely.
2. Mix the spinach with the cheese and egg yolks. Season with salt, pepper and nutmeg to taste.
3. Whisk the egg whites in a clean, grease-free bowl, with a rotary or balloon whisk, until they form soft peaks.
4. Heat a non-stick omelette pan until it's quite hot and you can feel a good heat rising. Add the oil and wipe round the pan quickly with kitchen paper.
5. Quickly and lightly fold the egg whites into the spinach mixture and pour into the heated pan.
6. Turn the heat down to medium and cook until the base is set and the top still is a little creamy. Hold the pan over a warmed plate and, using a palette knife, fold the omelette in half and slide it straight out of the pan.

Per serving: **P** **4½**

Brunch Kebabs

Serves 2

Preparation and cooking time: 20 minutes
Calories per serving: 190

Freezing not recommended

When you want to spoil yourself with a leisurely breakfast, treat yourself to this grilled version of a traditional cooked breakfast – much healthier than a fry-up! Skewering foods on a satay stick helps hold them together and makes the cooking easier. Serve with some crusty bread.

2 lamb's kidneys
3 lean rashers of back bacon
6 button mushrooms
1/2 green, red or yellow pepper
6 cherry tomatoes
1 small onion, quartered
2 teaspoons sunflower or olive oil
a good pinch of dried thyme
salt and freshly ground black pepper

1. If your skewers are wooden, soak them in water for half an hour to stop them from burning under the grill.
2. Halve the kidneys lengthways. Peel off the thin membranes and, using kitchen scissors, cut out the cores.
3. Cut the bacon rashers in half and roll each piece up. Trim any thick stalks from the mushrooms.
4. Cut the pepper into squares about the same size as the bacon rolls. Score a cross on the base of each tomato, and separate the onion quarters into segments.
5. Skewer the ingredients, alternating the different sorts. Brush with the oil, season to taste and sprinkle over the thyme.
6. Cover and chill until ready to serve. Preheat the grill until hot, and then turn the heat down to medium. Cook for about 4 minutes on the first side, and 3 minutes on the other.

Per serving: **P** 5½
Total per recipe: **P** 11

Lentil Kedgeree

Serves 4

Preparation time: 12 minutes
Cooking time: 25 minutes
Calories per serving: 355

Freezing recommended

The original kedgeree was an Indian dish of rice and lentils called 'kitchiri'; how the lentils came to be replaced by smoked haddock is a great culinary mystery! This dish is extremely healthy as lentils and rice form a high-carbohydrate low-fat meal that is packed with protein. It tastes very good too.

1 tablespoon sunflower oil
1 onion, chopped
2 garlic cloves, crushed
1–2 teaspoons mild curry powder
240 g (8 oz) easy-cook basmati rice
2 whole cloves
2 bay leaves
1 small cinnamon stick (optional)
1 litre (1¾ pint) vegetable stock or water
420 g (14 oz) canned lentils, drained
15 g (½ oz) butter or sunflower margarine
2 tablespoons chopped fresh parsley or coriander
salt and freshly ground black pepper

1. In a large non-stick saucepan, heat the oil until nice and hot and then add the onion and garlic. Turn the heat down, cover and cook gently for 3 minutes, until soft.
2. Stir in the curry powder, cook for a few seconds and then mix in the rice and cook for a minute or two.
3. Add the cloves, bay leaves and cinnamon, if using. Stir in the stock and about 1 teaspoon of salt. Bring to the boil, cover and turn the heat right down.
4. Simmer gently for 15 minutes, uncover and stir in the lentils and butter or sunflower margarine. Check the seasoning and cook for a few minutes more, to heat through.
5. If you wish you can remove the whole spices and bay leaf, although in India these are served with the dish as garnish. Lightly mix in the fresh herbs before serving.

Per serving: **P** 5½
Total per recipe: **P** 22

Spaghetti Amatriciana

Serves 2

Preparation time: 12 minutes
Cooking time: 20 minutes
Calories per serving: 310

Freezing recommended for sauce

This is a classic Italian tomato and smoky bacon sauce with just a little hint of Tabasco (although you can omit this if you're not fond of spicy foods).

2 teaspoons olive oil
1 rasher of lean back smoked bacon, chopped
1 small onion, chopped
1/2 red pepper, chopped
1 large garlic clove, crushed
1 tablespoon dry white wine (optional)
210 g (7 oz) canned chopped tomatoes
2–3 drops of Tabasco sauce (optional)
a good pinch of dried marjoram or oregano
120 g (4 oz) spaghetti
1 tablespoon chopped fresh parsley, to serve (optional)
salt and freshly ground black pepper

1. Heat a medium-sized saucepan; when hot add the oil and toss in the bacon, stirring until just cooked. This will take about 1 minute.
2. Turn the heat down, and add the onion, pepper, garlic and wine, if using. Stir well, cover and cook for 5 minutes over a gentle heat, shaking the pan occasionally.
3. Stir in the tomatoes, Tabasco sauce, if using, dried herbs, seasoning and 4 tablespoons of water. Simmer, uncovered, for 5 minutes, until slightly reduced. Set aside.
4. Cook the spaghetti according to the packet instructions and drain, but don't shake too much. In Italy, pasta is served slightly wet so there is less need to add extra oil.
5 Toss in the sauce and serve on warmed plates. Sprinkle with a little chopped parsley.

Per serving: **P** **5½**
Total per recipe: **P** **11**

Haddock and Sweetcorn Pasta

Serves 4

Preparation time: 10 minutes
Cooking time: 15 minutes
Calories per serving: 405

Freezing recommended

This is a simple, but very tasty, supper dish.

240 g (8 oz) smoked haddock
600 ml (1 pint) skimmed milk
1 tablespoon sunflower oil
1 onion, sliced
2 celery sticks, sliced thinly
1 small green or red pepper, sliced thinly
2 tablespoons flour
210 g (7 oz) canned sweetcorn kernels, drained
1 teaspoon dried mixed herbs
240 g (8 oz) pasta shapes
15 g (1/2 oz) freshly grated parmesan (optional)
1 punnet of mustard and cress, snipped
salt and freshly ground black pepper

1. Place the haddock in a large saucepan and pour in the milk. Bring to a boil, cover and turn the heat right down. Poach the fish for just 5 minutes.
2. Remove the fish from the pan and skin and flake it. Drain the poaching milk into a jug. Wipe out the pan and add the oil.
3. Heat this well and then stir in the onion, celery and pepper. Cover and turn the heat right down. Cook for 5 minutes until the vegetables have softened.
4. Sprinkle in the flour and stir. Cook for a few seconds and then gradually mix in the reserved poaching milk. Bring to the boil, stirring constantly, and simmer for a minute or two.
5. Add the sweetcorn, herbs, flaked fish and seasoning. Set aside and keep warm.
6. Cook the pasta according to the packet instructions. Drain but leave slightly wet. Toss into the haddock sauce, stirring well. Reheat gently and serve in a warmed dish, sprinkled with the parmesan cheese, if using, and snipped cress.

Per serving: **P** **6**
Total per recipe: **P** **24**

Club Sandwich

Serves 1

Preparation and cooking time: 12 minutes
Calories per serving: 365

Freezing not recommended

This is a real meal of a sandwich – three slices of bread with lean chicken or turkey, bacon and salad vegetables in between. Light rye or Granary bread will complement the other flavours best.

1 lean rasher of back bacon, trimmed of fat
45 g (1½ oz) cooked chicken or turkey
3 teaspoons low-Calorie mayonnaise
3 thin slices of rye or Granary bread
1 tomato, sliced thinly
2 lettuce leaves
1 small dill pickle, sliced

1. Grill the bacon rasher lightly until just cooked. Drain on kitchen paper. Shred the chicken or turkey meat.
2. Spread the mayonnaise on the bread slices. Make a triple decker sandwich, placing bacon on one layer and poultry on the other.
3. Divide the tomato, lettuce and pickle between the two layers and then sandwich everything together. Cut in diagonal quarters and serve skewered with cocktail sticks.

Per serving: P 8½

Muffin Pizzas

Serves 1

Preparation and cooking time: 10 minutes
Calories per serving: 495

Freezing not recommended

Ⓥ **if using vegetarian cheese**

These are very quick and easy. Wholemeal muffins are toasted and topped with pizza-style ingredients for a simple knife and fork snack.

2 wholemeal muffins
2 tomatoes, sliced thinly
60 g (2 oz) mozzarella cheese, cut in small cubes
a few thin slices of red or white onion
4 stoned black olives, sliced
2 good pinches of dried oregano
2 teaspoons grated parmesan cheese
salt and freshly ground black pepper

1. Preheat the grill. Split the muffins in half and toast lightly on both sides.
2. Top with the tomato slices, mozzarella cubes, and the onion and olive slices. Sprinkle with oregano, seasoning and parmesan.
3. Return to the grill and cook until the cheese just starts to bubble and everything is piping hot. Serve immediately.

Per serving: P 10½

Main Meals

Feeding the family no longer has to be a daunting prospect – even while following your weight-loss programme! Gone are the days when you had to prepare a pitiful little offering for yourself and serve the family their normal hefty meals. With 1,2,3 Success many of your favourite dishes can be prepared in ways that cut down on Points, yet still have the family asking for more.

Even entertaining is a breeze. Serve your guests any of the delicious recipes in this chapter and fill up their plates with fresh vegetables and lots of satisfying rice, pasta or potatoes.

Here you'll find some of our most popular family dishes and some more exotic recipes. As more and more of us take holidays to far-flung destinations, it's nice to be able to recreate at home some of the tastes we've enjoyed. You'll probably find that the herbs, spices and sauces you need are readily available in local supermarkets, and that a little often goes a long way.

If you're cooking for one or two, there's no need to miss out on good wholesome meals; most of the dishes in this chapter will freeze, so simply divide them up and don't forget to label them. One dark frozen block looks pretty much the same as another!

Mighty Mushrooms with Provençal Vegetables

Serves 4

Preparation time: 10 minutes
Cooking time: 30 minutes
Calories per serving: 80

Freezing not recommended

 if using vegetarian cheese

When you see those lovely large 'field' mushrooms in the shops, do buy them for this dish. This is a great vegetarian main meal. Serve with some new potatoes or crusty bread and some lightly boiled shredded cabbage.

4 large 'field' mushrooms
1 large courgette, chopped finely
1 small onion, sliced
½ small red or yellow pepper, chopped
2 teaspoons olive oil
a good pinch of dried thyme
45 g (1½ oz) low-fat Cheddar, grated
salt and freshly ground black pepper

1. Chop the mushrooms stalks and put them in a saucepan with the courgette, onion and pepper. Add the oil and 4 tablespoons of water.
2. Bring to the boil and add the thyme and seasoning. Cover and simmer gently for 10 minutes until softened, stirring once or twice. Drain, reserving the juices.
3. Preheat the oven to Gas Mark 4/180°C/350°F. Place the mushrooms, cup-side up, in a shallow roasting pan and trickle over the reserved vegetable juices. Season, cover with foil and bake for 15 minutes.
4. Uncover, spoon the vegetable filling into the centre of the mushrooms, sprinkle over the cheese and return to the oven for a further 10–15 minutes, until the cheese just melts and the vegetables are hot.

Per serving: **P 1**
Total per recipe: **P 4**

Cabbage and Lentil Rolls

Serves 6

Preparation time: 10 minutes
Cooking time: 25 minutes
Calories per serving: 90

Freezing not recommended

 if using vegetarian cheese

The outer leaves of a large cabbage are something that normally we might very well discard, but in this recipe they are transformed by filling them with a tasty lentil mixture. This makes a great protein-packed, vegetarian supper.

6 large cabbage leaves
420 g (14 oz) canned green lentils
30 g (1 oz) fresh breadcrumbs
2 teaspoons sunflower or olive oil
1 onion, chopped
1 garlic clove, crushed
420 g (14 oz) canned chopped tomatoes
1/2 teaspoon dried mixed herbs
4 tablespoons 0%-fat fromage frais
2 teaspoons fresh grated parmesan
salt and freshly ground black pepper

1. Cut the thick central rib from the cabbage leaves and blanch the leaves for 3 minutes in a large pan of boiling salted water.
2. Drain and immediately plunge into a big bowl of very cold water. Drain again and pat dry with kitchen paper.
3. Put the lentils in a bowl and mash with a fork. Stir in the breadcrumbs. Preheat the oven to Gas Mark 4/180°C/350°F.
4. Heat the oil in a saucepan and gently cook the onion and garlic for 5 minutes. Add the tomatoes, herbs and seasoning.
5. Simmer for 10 minutes. Mix a third of the tomato sauce into the lentils-and-crumb mixture. Season well.
6. Divide the filling between the leaves, fold in the sides and roll up. Place, join-side down, in a shallow ovenproof dish and reheat in the oven for 10 minutes.
7. Reheat the remaining sauce. Serve the rolls on warmed plates. Spoon the tomato sauce around the rolls, top with fromage frais and sprinkle with parmesan.

Per serving: **P 1½**
Total per recipe: **P 9**

Fish Timbales

Serves 4

Preparation time: 15 minutes
+ cooling + standing
Cooking time: 35 minutes
Calories per serving: 175

Freezing not recommended

This is easy to prepare and very impressive to look at. Fillets of plaice are given a filling of basmati rice, and are served with a pepper and tomato sauce; it's ideal for entertaining. Serve with a green vegetable. You will need ramekins for this as well as a low-fat cooking spray.

2 × 240 g (8 oz) plaice, filleted and skinned
salt and freshly ground black pepper
For the filling:
60 g (2 oz) basmati rice
210 ml (7 fl oz) vegetable stock or water
a good pinch of ground turmeric
1 tablespoon chopped fresh parsley
1 tablespoon chopped fresh chives
1 teaspoon low-fat spread
For the sauce:
1 red pepper, chopped
1 large tomato, chopped
180 ml (6 fl oz) vegetable stock or water

1. Line the bases of four medium-sized ramekins with discs of greaseproof paper. Spray evenly and lightly with cooking spray.
2. Cut each fillet in four lengthways, so you have eight long fillets. Season.
3. Put the rice, stock or water, turmeric and seasoning into a small saucepan. Bring to the boil and cover. Turn the heat down to a simmer. Cook gently for 12 minutes. Do not lift the lid.
4. Allow the rice to stand uncovered for 5 minutes, and then stir in the herbs and low-fat spread. Cool. Preheat the oven to Gas Mark 5/190°C/375°F.
5. Curl the fish fillets around inside the ramekins with the skinned side facing inwards. Allow two fillets per ramekin. Spoon the rice into the centre and press down lightly.
6. Place the ramekins on a baking sheet and cover each loosely with foil. Bake for 20 minutes, until the fish feels just firm. Allow to stand for 5 minutes.
7. Meanwhile, make the sauce. Place the pepper, tomato, stock and some seasoning in a saucepan. Simmer for 10 minutes, until the pepper and tomato are softened.
8. Purée in a blender or food processor until smooth. (For a smoother sauce, you can, if you wish, rub this purée though a sieve.)
9. Turn the timbales out by running a knife round the inside of each ramekin and shaking the timbales out on to four warmed plates. Spoon the sauce around them and serve.

Per serving: **P 2**
Total per recipe: **P 8**

Grilled Cod with Mediterranean Mash

Serves 4

Preparation time: 12 minutes
Cooking time: 20 minutes
Calories per serving: 200

Freezing not recommended

You could call this a healthier version of fish and chips! Cod is a lovely 'meaty' fish. Buy chunky-cut fillets or steaks. The potatoes are crushed and flavoured with olive and tomato.

4 × 120 g (4 oz) cod fillets or steaks, skinned
juice of ½ lemon
480 g (1 lb) new potatoes, halved
4 teaspoons low-fat olive oil spread
2 tablespoons stoned black olives, sliced
2 tomatoes, chopped
a little garlic salt, to taste
1 tablespoon chopped fresh chives or parsley
freshly ground black pepper

1. Season the fish, sprinkle with the lemon juice and set aside.
2. Boil the potatoes until tender. Drain and crush lightly with a fork. Mix in half the olive oil spread, the olives, tomatoes, garlic salt, pepper and fresh herbs. You should have a chunky purée. Set aside and keep warm.
3. Heat the grill until hot. Dot the top of the fish with the remaining spread. Turn down the heat to medium and grill the fish for 3–5 minutes on each side. Turn it carefully so the fish does not break up. Serve on warmed plates, topped with extra ground black pepper, with the crushed potatoes.

Per serving: **P 3½**
Total per recipe: **P 14**

Lamb Chops with Honey-mustard Glaze

Serves 4

Preparation time: 10 minutes
Cooking time: 10–15 minutes
Calories per serving: 395

Freezing not recommended

Use either neck cutlets or chump chops for this recipe and make sure you trim the fat off before cooking. These are delicious served with a low-Point accompaniment, such as light creamy potatoes beaten with hot skimmed milk and a knob of low-fat spread.

8 best-end neck cutlets or 4 chump chops
2 tablespoons clear honey
1 tablespoon coarse-grained mustard
1 small green cabbage, preferably Savoy or Sugar Loaf, shredded finely
2 teaspoons low-fat spread
a little freshly grated nutmeg
salt and freshly ground black pepper

1. Preheat the grill until hot. Grill the cutlets or chops for about 2 minutes on each side. Turn the heat down and remove the grill pan from the grill.
2. Mix the honey and mustard together and brush liberally on one side of the meat. Grill for another 3 minutes, although the thinner cutlets may need less cooking (see below).
3. Brush the other side with the honey-mustard glaze and grill for 2–3 minutes more.
4. Meanwhile, blanch the cabbage in a pan of salted boiling water for just 3 minutes. Drain well and return to the pan with the low-fat spread, seasoning and nutmeg to taste. Serve with the lamb chops.

Cook's note:
Timings depend on how pink or well done you like your meat. You can check the doneness while the meat cooks; pink lamb will feel slightly springy when pressed with a finger, well-done lamb will be firm. Be careful not to overcook lamb as it will become tough.

Per serving: **P 3½**
Total per recipe: **P 14**

Mexican Bean Tortillas

Makes 4

Preparation time: 15 minutes
Cooking time: 15 minutes
Calories per serving: 210

Freezing not recommended

V if using vegetarian cheese

Mexican food is becoming popular and no wonder. It is full of wonderful flavours and texture combinations, but also it's great fun to eat.

4 wheat tortillas
1 onion, sliced
1 small red pepper, sliced
2 garlic cloves, crushed
2 teaspoons sunflower oil
2 teaspoons mild chilli powder
$\frac{1}{2}$ teaspoon ground cumin
$\frac{1}{2}$ teaspoon dried oregano
420 g (14 oz) canned chopped
　tomatoes
210 g (7 oz) canned red kidney
　beans, drained
4 tablespoons Quark (skimmed
　milk soft cheese)
2 tablespoons low-fat Cheddar,
　grated
lettuce leaves, to serve
salt and freshly ground black
　pepper

1. Wrap the tortillas in foil and place in a low oven to warm through.
2. Put the onion, pepper and garlic in a saucepan with the oil and 2 tablespoons of water. Bring to a boil, and cover. Simmer gently for 5 minutes, until softened.
3. Stir in the spices and oregano, and cook for a few seconds. Add the tomatoes. Season well and bring to a boil. Simmer, uncovered, for 10 minutes, until reduced and thickened.
4. Stir in the beans and cook for a few minutes more.
5. Unwrap the tortillas and lay them on a worktop. Spread some bean sauce on each, dollop with the Quark, and sprinkle on some cheese. Roll up and place, join-side down, on a serving plate lined with lettuce leaves. Eat using your fingers and plenty of napkins.

Cook's note:
Wheat tortillas can be bought from many supermarkets and freeze very well unfilled.

Per serving: **P** 3½
Total per recipe: **P** 14

Ratatouille Cannelloni

Serves 4

Preparation time: 15 minutes
+ draining aubergines
Cooking time: 30 minutes
Calories per serving: 180

Freezing not recommended

V if using vegetarian cheese

Instead of making a time-consuming lasagne, use the same ingredients and serve them as an easy cannelloni. Try not to overcook the vegetables. They taste much nicer served with a bit of bite.

1 small aubergine, chopped
8 lasagne sheets
1 tablespoon olive oil
1 onion, chopped
2 courgettes, chopped
1 red or yellow pepper,
　de-seeded and chopped
2 garlic cloves, crushed
420 g (14 oz) canned chopped
　tomatoes
2 tablespoons shredded fresh
　basil
210 g (7 oz) 0%-fat fromage
　frais
2 tablespoons freshly grated
　parmesan cheese
salt and freshly ground black
　pepper

1. Put the chunks of aubergine in a colander and sprinkle with some salt. Leave to drain over a sink for 20 minutes. Rinse in cold water and pat dry with kitchen paper; this will get rid of any bitter juices.
2. Meanwhile, blanch the pasta sheets, three or four at a time in plenty of salted boiling water, stirring occasionally so they don't stick together. Remove them with a slotted spoon and put in a large bowl of very cold water. Drain and pat dry with kitchen paper.
3. Heat the oil in a large saucepan and add the aubergine, onion, courgettes, pepper and garlic. Stir so all the vegetables are coated in oil. Add 4 tablespoons of water. Cover and simmer very gently for 5 minutes, shaking the pan occasionally.
4. Stir in the chopped tomatoes, seasoning and basil. Simmer uncovered for 5–10 minutes, until the liquid has reduced. Preheat the oven to Gas Mark 4/180°C/350°F.
5. Divide the filling between the pasta sheets and roll them up. Place join-side down in a shallow dish. Cover with foil and reheat in the oven for 10 minutes.
6. Serve topped with dollops of the fromage frais and sprinkled with parmesan.

Per serving: **P** 3½
Total per recipe: **P** 14

Chicken in a Parcel

Serves 2

Preparation time: 10 minutes
Cooking time: 20 minutes
Calories per serving: 200

Freezing not recommended

In this recipe, chicken breasts
are wrapped in greaseproof
paper or foil before cooking
so they are moist and tender
without using any extra fat.
The juices that collect in the
parcel make a delicious light
sauce for the meat.

1 small leek, sliced very thinly
120 g (4 oz) button
 mushrooms, sliced thinly
2 tablespoons dry white wine,
 dry vermouth or dry sherry
2 teaspoons low-fat spread
2 × 120 g (4 oz) boneless,
 skinless chicken breasts
2 thin slices of lean ham
1 tablespoon chopped fresh
 parsley
salt and freshly ground black
 pepper

1. Preheat the oven to Gas Mark 5/190°C/375°F. Prepare two sheets
of greaseproof paper or foil about 25 cm (10 inches) square. If using
greaseproof paper, then dip it into cold water to soften it.
2. Put the leek, mushrooms, alcohol and low-fat spread into a small
pan and cook for 3 minutes, stirring until the vegetables are softened.
Season well.
3. Make a slit in the side of each chicken breast. Insert a piece of
ham and close.
4. Lay the sheets of paper or foil on a worktop. Spoon the leek and
mushroom mixture in the centre and place a breast on top. Season
and trickle over any pan juices.
5. Wrap the parcel up, folding over the edges so that no liquid can
escape. Place, join-side uppermost, on a baking sheet and bake for
about 15 minutes until the chicken feels quite firm when pressed.
6. Unwrap carefully on to warm serving places and trickle over the
juices and vegetables. Sprinkle with parsley and serve hot.

Per serving: **P 4**
Total per recipe: **P 8**

Chinese Liver Stir-fry

Serves 3

Preparation time: 10 minutes
Calories per serving: 275

Freezing not recommended

Liver is an excellent source
of protein and iron, and low
in fat. It's also quite delicious
served as a Chinese-style
stir-fry. Try this with some
medium egg noodles or
some plain boiled rice.

227 g packet of frozen chicken
 livers, thawed well
2 tablespoons sunflower oil
1 red pepper, sliced thinly
1 leek, sliced thinly
1 carrot, grated coarsely
2 garlic cloves, crushed
1 cm ($\frac{1}{2}$-inch) piece of fresh
 root ginger, grated
$\frac{1}{2}$ teaspoon five-spice powder
2 teaspoons sesame seeds
For the sauce:
3 tablespoons dark soy sauce,
 preferably Japanese-style
 (e.g. Kikkoman)
1 tablespoon dry sherry
1 teaspoon sesame oil
a pinch of caster sugar

1. Pat the chicken livers dry with kitchen paper and chop any large
pieces into bite-sized chunks.
2. In a large non-stick wok or frying-pan, heat the oil well and
quickly stir-fry the livers for about 2 minutes until well browned.
Remove with a slotted spoon.
3. Add the red pepper, leek and carrot and 3 tablespoons of water.
Stir and toss for 4 minutes until lightly cooked and softened, but
still crisp.
4. Stir in the garlic and ginger, tossing for a few seconds. Return the
livers to the pan and sprinkle with the five-spice powder.
5. Quickly mix the sauce ingredients together in a cup and pour
into the wok. Toss everything together, scatter with the sesame
seeds and serve immediately.

Per serving: **P 4**
Total per recipe: **P 12**

Quick Fish Crumble

Serves 3

Preparation time: 15 minutes
Cooking time: 40 minutes
Calories per serving: 235

Freezing recommended

This is a very simple and tasty version of fish pie which makes use of frozen fish steaks.

2 × 90 g (3 oz) frozen fish
  steaks, thawed
1 large leek, sliced thinly
1 carrot, chopped finely
75 g (2½ oz) button
  mushrooms, sliced
2 teaspoons sunflower oil
300 ml (½ pint) skimmed milk
1 tablespoon cornflour
1 tablespoon chopped fresh
  parsley
a good squeeze of lemon juice
1 tomato, sliced
salt and freshly ground black
  pepper
For the crumble topping:
30 g (1 oz) plain flour
30 g (1 oz) wholemeal flour
½ teaspoon dried thyme
4 teaspoons low-fat margarine

1. Cut each fish steak into six pieces. Put the leek, carrot and mushrooms in a saucepan with the oil and 2 tablespoons of water.
2. Bring to the boil, cover and simmer gently for 5 minutes, or until softened.
3. Blend a little milk with the cornflour to make a thin paste. Add the rest of the milk to the vegetables. Bring to the boil and slowly trickle in the cornflour paste, stirring well until smooth and thickened.
4. Season well and add the parsley and lemon juice. Put the fish in a shallow pie dish and cover with the sauce.
5. Preheat the oven to Gas Mark 5/190°C/375°F. Mix together the plain and wholemeal flour, the thyme and some seasoning. Rub in the low-fat margarine so that the mixture resembles breadcrumbs.
6. Sprinkle the crumble topping over the fish and arrange the tomato slices around the edge. Bake for 30 minutes, until golden brown. Serve hot.

Per serving: **P 4**
Total per recipe: **P 12**

Spiced Beef and Winter Vegetable Casserole

Serves 4

Preparation time: 10 minutes
Cooking time: 1¼ hours
Calories per serving: 165

Freezing recommended

This is a real winter warmer of a casserole; it's also really easy to prepare and, once it's been popped in the oven, it can be left to cook slowly without further attention. Serve with some boiled potatoes, pasta or rice. You can substitute diced turkey for the stewing beef. This will reduce the cooking time to 45 minutes.

300 g (10 oz) lean stewing beef, cut into small cubes
2 teaspoons sunflower oil
1 carrot, chopped
1 parsnip, chopped
1 celery stick, sliced
1 leek, sliced
1 teaspoon ground coriander
½ teaspoon ground cinnamon
½ teaspoon ground cumin
1 tablespoon flour
1 tablespoon Worcestershire sauce
½ teaspoon dried oregano or a good pinch of dried thyme
1 tablespoon tomato purée
300 ml (½ pint) stock
salt and freshly ground black pepper

1. Preheat the oven to Gas Mark 4/180°C/350°F. Heat a non-stick pan until quite hot and dry-fry the meat for 3 minutes, stirring until browned. Remove with a slotted spoon and set aside.
2. Add the oil to the pan and heat. Stir in all the vegetables and add 2 tablespoons of water. Cook gently for 5 minutes, until softened.
3. Mix in the spices and cook for a few seconds. Stir in the flour, Worcestershire sauce, oregano or thyme, tomato purée and seasoning.
4. Return the meat to the pan and pour in the stock. Bring to the boil, stirring. Transfer to an ovenproof casserole dish. Cover and cook for 1½ hours until the meat is tender.

Cook's note:
Casseroles are nicest if made a day ahead and reheated. The flavours have an opportunity to mature and any excess fat can be removed from the top when the casserole is chilled.

Per serving: **P** 4½
Total per recipe: **P** 18

Spiced Roast Vegetables and Chick-peas

Serves 4

Preparation time: 15 minutes
Cooking time: 1 hour
Calories per serving: 345

Freezing recommended

Roasting root vegetables in a hot oven gives them a deliciously, slightly smoky flavour, and the chick-peas add extra protein and fibre. For a little embellishment you could serve this dish with dollops of low-fat bio yogurt and maybe some light, crisp shreds of boiled cabbage.

480 g (1 lb) potatoes, scrubbed
240 g (8 oz) parsnips, peeled
240 g (8 oz) swede, peeled
240 g (8 oz) carrots, peeled
2 tablespoons sunflower or olive oil
1 large onion, quartered
1 large green pepper, sliced thickly
2 teaspoons cumin seeds, crushed, or ground cumin
2 teaspoons ground coriander
2 teaspoons garam masala or mild curry powder
½ teaspoon dried thyme
420 g (14 oz) canned chick-peas, drained
2 tablespoons chopped fresh mint, parsley or coriander
salt and freshly ground black pepper

1. Cut the root vegetables into small, even-sized chunks. Bring a large pan of water to the boil and blanch the vegetables for 5 minutes. Drain well.
2. Preheat the oven to Gas Mark 6/200°C/400°F. Put the oil in a roasting pan and heat in the oven.
3. In a large bowl, mix together the blanched vegetables, the onion segments, pepper slices, cumin, coriander, garam masala or curry powder and thyme.
4. Place them in a single layer in the roasting pan and stir to coat them well with the hot oil. Season well.
5. Bake for about 45 minutes, turning occasionally until the vegetables are nice and crisp. Mix in the chick-peas and return to the oven for a further 10 minutes. Serve hot.

Per serving: **P** 4½
Total per recipe: **P** 18

Mince Hot-pot

Serves 4

Preparation time: 15 minutes
Cooking time: 1 hour 20 minutes
Calories per serving: 345

Freezing recommended

A hot-pot is the sort of dish that all the family can enjoy. This version is very low in fat and fits in perfectly with your weight-loss Programme; it's ideal for freezing too. Make sure you buy very lean mince – either beef, turkey or lamb will be delicious. Serve with no-Points green steamed vegetables such as brussels sprouts, spinach or beans.

480 g (1 lb) potatoes, sliced very thinly
480 g (1 lb) very lean beef, turkey or lamb mince
1 carrot, grated coarsely
1 small celery stick, chopped finely
420 ml (14 fl oz) stock
1 tablespoon flour
1 tablespoon soy sauce
1 tablespoon Worcestershire sauce
a good pinch of dried mixed herbs
2 teaspoons low-fat spread, melted
1 tablespoon dried breadcrumbs
salt and freshly ground black pepper

1. Blanch the potato slices in a large pan of boiling water for 2 minutes, then drain.
2. Heat a large non-stick pan until very hot and then dry-fry the mince, stirring frequently to break up any lumps.
3. Add the vegetables to the pan and stir. Add 2 tablespoons of the stock. Cook for 5 minutes until the vegetables have softened, and then stir in the flour and soy and Worcestershire sauces.
4. Cook for 1 minute. Mix in the remaining stock, the herbs and seasoning. Bring to a boil, turn down to a simmer and cook uncovered for 15 minutes, stirring occasionally.
5. Preheat the oven to Gas Mark 6/200°C/400°F. Transfer the mince to a shallow ovenproof dish, top with the potato slices and brush with the melted low-fat spread. Sprinkle over the breadcrumbs and bake for 45 minutes to 1 hour, or until the top is golden brown.

Per serving: **P 5**
Total per recipe: **P 20**

Thai Chicken Curry

Serves 3

Preparation time: 10 minutes + 20 minutes soaking
Cooking time: 30 minutes
Calories per serving: 260

Freezing recommended

Thai-style curries taste lighter and fresher than Indian ones, since they are made with fresh spices rather than dried ones. Use boneless and skinless chicken thighs, which are tasty and economical. Try serving this aromatic dish with plain boiled Thai rice, which is slightly sticky and a perfect accompaniment.

15 g (½ oz) desiccated coconut
450 ml (¾ pint) boiling water
6 boneless, skinless chicken thighs (about 480 g/1 lb)
120 g (4 oz) potato, chopped
½ teaspoon freshly grated nutmeg
salt and freshly ground black pepper
2 tablespoons chopped fresh coriander or parsley, to serve
For the curry paste:
1 small onion, chopped
2 garlic cloves, crushed
1 lemon grass stalk, chopped finely, or 1 teaspoon lemon grass paste, or grated zest of 1 lemon
1 cm (½-inch) piece of fresh root ginger, chopped
2–3 fresh green chillies, de-seeded, or 2–3 teaspoons green chilli paste
1 tablespoon ground coriander
1 teaspoon ground cumin

1. Mix the coconut and boiling water together and leave to soak for 20 minutes, then drain. Reserve the water but discard the coconut.
2. Purée all the curry paste ingredients together in a blender or food processor, adding a little coconut water to moisten it. Alternatively, grind together using a pestle and mortar.
3. Trim the chicken thighs of any visible fat and cut into bite-sized pieces.
4. Put the curry-paste purée into a large saucepan and simmer for 3 minutes.
5. Pour in the remaining coconut water and bring to the boil, stirring. Add the chicken and potatoes, plus some seasoning and the nutmeg.
6. Turn the heat down to a gentle simmer and cook, uncovered, for 25 minutes, until the meat is tender and the potatoes very soft. Sprinkle over the chopped fresh herbs and serve.

Per serving: **P 5**
Total per recipe: **P 15**

Salmon with Sweet and Sour Pepper Sauce

Serves 4

Preparation time: 12 minutes
Cooking time: 20 minutes
Calories per serving: 275

Freezing not recommended

Fresh farmed salmon is now a comparable price to white fish and makes a wonderful, not-too-expensive special-occasion meal. It's a healthy choice, since it's high in omega-3 fatty acids which help prevent heart disease. Serve these grilled salmon cutlets with this easy and colourful pepper sauce.

4 x 120 g (4 oz) salmon cutlets
juice of ½ lemon
2 teaspoons low-fat olive
   oil spread
For the sauce:
1 large red pepper, de-seeded
   and chopped
1 large yellow pepper,
   de-seeded and chopped
1 small onion, chopped
1 tablespoon olive or
   sunflower oil
300 ml (½ pint) vegetable stock
2 tablespoons dry vermouth or
   dry white wine
1 teaspoon white wine vinegar
¼ teaspoon dried tarragon
a pinch of dried thyme
2–3 fresh basil leaves
1 bay leaf
1 tablespoon caster sugar
salt and freshly ground black
   pepper
4 sprigs of fresh basil, to
   garnish (optional)

1. Season the cutlets, sprinkle with lemon juice and set aside.
2. Put the peppers, onions and olive or sunflower oil in a saucepan with 2 tablespoons of stock. Cover and cook over a gentle heat for 5 minutes, until softened.
3. Stir in the vermouth or wine and cook, uncovered, for about 2 minutes, until the liquid has reduced right down. Add the vinegar, remaining stock, herbs, sugar and seasoning.
4. Bring to the boil and simmer, uncovered, for 15 minutes, until the peppers are very soft. Remove the bay leaf.
5. Purée in a blender or food processor until smooth. Rub through a fine sieve with the back of a wooden spoon or ladle. Set aside and keep warm.
6. Preheat the grill until hot. Cook the salmon cutlets for about 3 minutes on each side, turning carefully. Serve with the sauce. You could garnish the dish with sprigs of fresh basil.

Per serving: **P 5**
Total per recipe: **P 20**

Spicy Egg Curry

Serves 3

Preparation time: 20 minutes
Cooking time: 20 minutes
Calories per serving: 315

Freezing not recommended

V if using free-range eggs

This egg curry is simplicity itself to make, and is served with aromatic basmati rice.

1 onion, sliced
1 small green pepper, sliced
1 large garlic clove, crushed
1 tablespoon grated fresh root ginger
2 teaspoons sunflower oil
1 tablespoon mild curry powder
2 tablespoons split red lentils
450 ml (³/₄ pint) vegetable stock
3 eggs, hard-boiled, peeled and quartered
90 g (3 oz) basmati rice
2 tablespoons chopped fresh parsley or coriander
1 teaspoon low-fat spread
salt and freshly ground black pepper
To serve:
2 teaspoons poppy seeds
2 popadams, grilled and crushed

1. Put the onion, pepper, garlic and ginger in a saucepan with the oil and 2 tablespoons of water. Stir, cover and cook gently for 5 minutes, until softened.
2. Stir in the curry powder, cook for a minute and then add the lentils and stock.
3. Bring to the boil and season well. Cover and simmer for 10 minutes. Uncover, cook for another 5 minutes, and then stir in the eggs. Cook just long enough to reheat and then set aside.
4. Meanwhile, cook the basmati according to the packet instructions. Drain and rinse in boiling water. Toss in the chopped herbs and the low-fat spread.
5. Spoon the rice on to a serving plate and top with the egg curry. Scatter the poppy seeds and crushed popadoms on top.

Per serving: **P** **5¹/₂**
Total per recipe: **P** **16¹/₂**

Jamaican Pork Chops

Serves 2

Preparation time: 10 minutes + marinating
Cooking time: 12 minutes
Calories per serving: 305

Freezing not recommended

This is a simple classic dish from Jamaica; you make a rich spicy paste and rub it into some lean pork chops. It's lovely served with plain boiled rice and a crisp green salad.

4 salad onions
1 fresh red or green chilli, de-seeded
1 large bay leaf
1 teaspoon ground cinnamon
4 whole cloves
¹/₂ teaspoon ground nutmeg
2 × 180 g (6 oz) lean pork chops, trimmed of all fat
salt and freshly ground black pepper

1. First make the paste. Put the onions, chilli, bay leaf, cinnamon, cloves, nutmeg and seasoning into a food processor. Grind to a smooth paste. Or simply chop the onion, chilli and bay leaf as finely as possible and mix with the spices.
2. Spread this paste on both sides of the chops. Refrigerate for at least an hour or preferably overnight.
3. Remove the chops from the marinade, scraping off any excess. Preheat the grill until hot and place the chops on a sheet of foil.
4. Turn the heat down to medium and cook the chops for about 5 minutes on each side. Be careful not to overcook or the meat will become tough. Serve hot.

Per serving: **P** **7¹/₂**
Total per recipe: **P** **15**

Desserts

Once upon a time, desserts were the dieter's dilemma but, with 1,2,3 Success, you can enjoy your favourite desserts in low-Points versions.

A light, fresh, fruit-based dessert can form an important part of a well-balanced eating plan. For a start, there is such a glorious range of fruits available all round the year, as well as canned fruits in natural juices. You can easily replace many of the ingredients of conventional puds with lighter products and save yourself a Point or two. For example, use artificial sweetener instead of sugar; instead of cream use low-fat yogurt, fromage frais, smetana, low-fat soft cheese – there are even low-fat creams available now! Low-fat frozen desserts can be served either on their own or transformed into exciting sundaes, with a quick, crunchy topping made of crushed biscuits or low-fat granola.

One piece of equipment that has quite transformed my own baking is reusable non-stick baking sheeting sold under a variety of brand names, but increasingly easy to buy. Another good buy is low-fat cooking spray. Both cut out the need to grease tins which means you can cook low-fat, or even no-fat sweet treats without the fear of them sticking.

Rhubarb and Banana Fool

Serves 4

Preparation time: 10 minutes
Cooking time: 7 minutes
Calories per serving: 110

Freezing not recommended

(V) if using a free-range egg

This is an old-fashioned fruit dessert that deserves reviving – it's wonderfully low in Points, but perfectly scrummy. Rhubarb is particularly well complemented by banana and a hint of ginger.

480 g (1 lb) pink rhubarb
2 teaspoon chopped stem ginger (optional)
artificial sweetener, to taste
1 ripe banana
150 g (5 oz) low-fat, Greek-style yogurt
3 tablespoons low-fat ready-made custard
1 egg white
1/2 square dark chocolate, grated

1. Trim and wash the rhubarb and cut into chunks. Cook gently in a small saucepan until it has completely softened – don't add any extra water. It doesn't matter if the rhubarb breaks up. If it appears a little watery, drain some liquid off.
2. Allow to cool and mix in the ginger, if using, and sweetener to taste. Purée in a blender or food processor until smooth. Slice in the banana and blend again.
3. Add the yogurt and the custard and blend again. Transfer to a bowl and chill.
4. Whisk the egg white until it forms soft peaks and carefully fold in. Spoon into four pretty serving dishes and top with the grated chocolate.

Variations:
Gooseberries also make excellent fools. Cook them in the same way as the rhubarb. Or you could use very ripe strawberries, which need no cooking at all.

Per serving: **P 1**
Total per recipe: **P 4**

Red Fruits with Frothy Orange Sauce

Serves 2

**Preparation and cooking
time:** 7 minutes + cooling

Calories per serving: 110

Freezing not recommended

 if using a free-range egg

120 g (4 oz) strawberries
120 g (4 oz) raspberries
juice of 1 small orange
1 egg
1 tablespoon caster sugar
1 teaspoon grated orange zest
a few drops of vanilla extract

**One egg is enough to make a
luscious summer dessert for
two people. The sauce takes
just minutes to make and is
best served still warm. You
will need an electric hand-
beater for this.**

1. Place the fruits in a bowl and sprinkle over the orange juice.
Leave to soak in the fridge.
2. When ready to serve, put a small pan of water on to boil. Place
the egg, sugar, orange zest and vanilla in a heatproof bowl that just
fits over the pan. When the water starts to boil put the bowl on top
of the pan and turn the heat down to a simmer.
3. Using a hand-beater, whisk the egg mixture on high speed until
you have a pale golden, firm foam. This will take about 3–5 minutes,
and you should be able to lift the mixture into high, stable peaks.
4. Remove the bowl from the heat and continue whisking for
another minute or so. Allow to cool for 5 minutes while you divide
the fruits between two pretty dishes.
5. Give the sauce one quick whisk again before you spoon it over
the fruits.

Per serving: **P 1½**
Total per recipe: **P 3**

Berry Jelly Loaf

Serves 6

Preparation time: 5 minutes
+ cooling and setting
Calories per serving: 90

Freezing not recommended

**This looks very pretty when
cut in slices. Use whatever
soft fruits are in season.**

600 ml (1 pint) cranberry and
   raspberry juice
1¹/₂ sachets gelatine
1 large ripe banana
240 g (8 oz) soft berry fruits
   (e.g. blueberries,
   strawberries, raspberries and
   blackberries)

1. Pour a little juice into a small bowl. Sprinkle over the gelatine
and stir. Leave to stand and 'sponge' for a few moments.
2. Heat the rest of the juice until almost boiling and then mix in
the sponged gelatine. Stir until dissolved. Allow to cool to room
temperature.
3. Pour a thin layer of liquid jelly into the base of a 480 g (1 lb) loaf
tin and chill until set.
4. Peel the banana and cut into quarters lengthways. Place the
banana strips lengthways on top of the set jelly and arrange the rest
of the fruit at random. Try and picture what the slices of the jelly
will look like when you cut into it. As you add the fruit, pour in the
jelly until it is all used up. Tap the loaf tin gently to get rid of any air
pockets. Return the jelly to the fridge carefully, without spilling any.
Chill until set and firm.
5. To serve, wet an oval serving plate with cold water (this allows
you to move the loaf to the correct position after it's come out of
the tin). Dip the tin into hot water and count to five. Loosen the
sides with a blunt knife, place the plate on top, invert and shake
out. You may have to repeat the procedure if it doesn't work the
first time. To serve, cut in slices, with an electric carving knife if you
have one.

Per serving: P 1¹/₂
Total per recipe: P 9

Plum and Mango Charlotte

Serves 4

Preparation time: 15 minutes
Cooking time: 30 minutes
Calories per serving: 165

Freezing recommended

**Serve warm with a little
ready-made low-fat custard.**

6 large, ripe plums
1 ripe mango
3 tablespoons orange juice
¹/₂ teaspoon ground cinnamon
4 slices wholemeal bread,
   crusts removed
2 teaspoons low-fat spread
1 tablespoon demerara sugar

1. Halve and stone the plums. Slice the fruit.
2. To prepare the mango, first peel thinly and then cut down either
side of the large flat stone in the centre. Slice the flesh. Cut away
any flesh from around the stone, too.
3. Place the fruit in a small pie dish and scatter over the orange
juice. Sprinkle with the cinnamon.
4. Spread the bread with the low-fat spread. Cut the bread into
triangles.
5. Arrange the bread on top of the fruit, 'buttered'-side up. Scatter
the demerara over the top. Place the dish on a baking sheet.
6. Preheat the oven to Gas Mark 5/190°C/375°F and bake for 25–30
minutes until lightly browned on top.

Cook's tip:
This pudding can be prepared ahead and baked just before you
need it.

Variations:
Instead of plums, try using fresh apricots when they are in season.
Instead of the mango, try using two ripe bananas.

Per serving: P 2
Total per recipe: P 8

Orange and Lemon Custards with Apple Crisps

Serves 2

Preparation time: 5 minutes
Cooking time: 45 minutes + drying
Calories per serving: 195

Freezing not recommended

V if using a free-range egg

Custards are very easy to make and need no attention while they're baking. Instead of biscuits, try serving them with these apple 'crisps'. The crisps can be stored for a few days in an airtight tin. For this you can use non-stick reusable baking sheets or low-fat cooking spray. If, instead, you use a small amount of fat to grease your pan, just add the extra Points.

1 Granny Smith apple, cored
1 tablespoon lemon juice
For the custard:
210 ml (7 fl oz) skimmed milk
20 g (³/₄ oz) caster sugar
¹/₂ teaspoon vanilla extract
1 strip of lemon zest
1 strip of orange zest
1 egg

1. First, make the apple crisps. Slice the apple into water-thin slices with a large, very sharp knife or, ideally, a mandolin.
2. Preheat the oven to its low or warm setting. Lay a non-stick baking sheet on a baking tray or use low-fat cooking spray – one squirt is enough. Spread the apple slices out – don't overlap them. Brush lightly with the lemon juice.
3. Put in the oven and let them dry out for about 45 minutes, until they become firm and pale golden brown. (If the oven is too hot then prop open the oven door.) Remove with a palette knife to a wire tray to crisp and cool.
4. Meanwhile, bring the milk and sugar to a boil. Remove from the heat and add the vanilla extract and the two strips of fruit zest. Leave to cool.
5. Raise the oven temperature to Gas Mark 3/170°C/325°F. Grease two medium-sized ramekins with low-fat spray and stand them in a small roasting dish.
6. Remove the zest strips from the milk. Beat the egg in a small bowl and whisk in the milk. Pour into the ramekins.
7. Pour hot water into the roasting tin to come half-way up the outsides of the ramekins and bake for about 45 minutes, until just set. Serve on pretty dessert plates, accompanied by the apple crisps.

Per serving: **P 2**
Total per recipe: **P 4**

Raspberry Scones

Makes 6

Preparation time: 15 minutes
Cooking time: 12 minutes
Calories per serving: 125

Freezing not recommended

This is a classic dessert –
crisp scones, split and served
still fresh and warm, filled
with a little cream and
raspberries.

105 g (3½ oz) plain flour
2 teaspoons caster sugar
a good pinch of salt
1½ teaspoons baking powder
30 g (1 oz) sunflower
    margarine
5 tablespoons skimmed milk
To serve:
120 g (4 oz) fresh raspberries
6 tablespoons half-fat cream
½ teaspoon icing sugar, to dust

1. Preheat the oven to Gas Mark 7/220°C/425°F.
2. Sift the flour, sugar, salt and baking powder into a bowl and rub
in the margarine until the mixture resembles fine breadcrumbs.
3. Mix in enough milk, lightly and quickly, to form a soft dough;
if it seems a little dry then add a little extra in cautious amounts,
alternatively, you may find you don't need it all – it depends on the
flour.
4. Roll out the dough on a lightly floured board to a 5 mm (¼-inch)
thickness. Cut out six 5 cm (2-inch) rounds.
5. Place on a non-stick baking sheet and bake for about 12 minutes,
until golden brown. Remove and cool on a wire tray.
6. To serve, split each scone in two and fill with the raspberries and
half-fat cream. Dust with a little icing sugar and serve while they are
still very slightly warm.

Per serving: **P** 2½
Total per recipe: **P** 15

Basmati Rice Pudding

Serves 3

Preparation time: 5 minutes
+ 30 minutes cooking
Calories per serving: 190

Freezing not recommended

Rice puddings don't have to
contain cream to be creamy.
The natural starch in the rice
will make them creamy.
Aromatic basmati rice makes
a lovely light dessert with
fewer Points or fat than a
traditional rice pudding.
Serve with a few sliced
strawberries.

60 g (2 oz) basmati rice
600 ml (1 pint) skimmed milk
45 g (1½ oz) caster sugar
3 cardamom pods
1 bay leaf
a little ground cinnamon

1. Put the rice, milk, sugar, cardamom pods and bay leaf into a
heavy-based non-stick saucepan. Bring to the boil, stirring constantly,
then reduce the heat to a very gentle simmer.
2. Cook for up to 30 minutes, stirring occasionally, until thick and
creamy and the rice is very soft. If the milk starts to evaporate too
much during cooking, simply add a little water and carry on cooking
gently. It will reduce again.
3. Cool, stirring occasionally. Remove the cardamom pods and bay
leaf. Spoon into pretty dishes and sprinkle with a little cinnamon.

Per serving: **P** 2½
Total per recipe: **P** 7½

Milk Shakes

Serves 1

Preparation time: 3–5 minutes
Calories per serving: 125

Freezing not recommended

Home-made milk shakes are quick, easy and nutritious; they're an ideal snack and a good way to use up some of your daily milk allowance. Vary the fruit and low-fat frozen dessert to suit your own tastes. The wheatgerm is a healthy addition.

150 ml (¼ pint) skimmed milk
2 tablespoons low-fat frozen dessert
60 g (2 oz) soft or ripe fruits (e.g. strawberries, raspberries, bananas, pears, apricots, mango or papaya)
1 teaspoon wheatgerm (optional)
a sprig of fresh mint (optional)

1. Put everything bar the mint into a blender and blend to a thick cream. If using a food processor, then purée the fruits first slowly, then pour in the milk with the machine running, and finally add the other ingredients.
2. Pour into a long glass (ideally lightly chilled) and decorate with a sprig of mint, if you like. Sip through a thick straw.

Variation:
Use fruit-flavoured diet yogurts, instead of frozen desserts, to make a yogurt shake.

> **Per serving: P 2½**

Hot Chocolate Soufflé

Serves 4

Preparation time: 10 minutes + cooling
Cooking time: 20–25 minutes
Calories per serving: 150

Freezing not recommended

 if using free-range eggs

Soufflés are not difficult to make and they're absolutely scrumptious to eat! The secret is to whisk the egg whites to a good firm foam and not to let them hang around. This sweet soufflé has a lovely chocolaty flavour.

2 tablespoons cocoa powder
1 teaspoon instant coffee powder
2 tablespoons plain flour
1 tablespoon low-fat spread
30 g (1 oz) soft brown sugar
210 ml (7 fl oz) milk
2 eggs, separated
½ teaspoon icing sugar

1. Sift the cocoa, coffee and flour together. Put in a large saucepan with the low-fat spread, brown sugar and milk. Bring slowly to the boil, whisking, until you have a smooth thick sauce.
2. Simmer for about half a minute and then remove and cool for 10 minutes. Preheat the oven to Gas Mark 5/190°C/375°F. Lightly grease the inside of a 600 ml (1-pint) soufflé dish with some low-fat spray.
3. Beat the egg yolks into the cocoa sauce. In a large, clean bowl, whisk the egg whites to a thick foam that will form and hold peaks when you lift the beaters up. Carefully fold the egg whites into the cocoa mixture, using a figure of eight movement. Spoon into the soufflé dish.
4. Bake for 20–25 minutes, until the soufflé has risen and the centre is slightly wobbly. (Don't open the oven door for the first 15 minutes of cooking and preferably not at all until the soufflé is done.)
5. Put the icing sugar in a small sieve and, as you pull the soufflé out of the oven, quickly sprinkle the sugar over the top. Serve immediately – a soufflé waits for no one!

> **Per serving: P 3**
> **Total per recipe: P 12**

Blackberry and Apple Trifle

Serves 4

Preparation time: 10 minutes
+ 30 minutes chilling
Calories per serving: 160

Freezing not recommended

This is an ideal Sunday pud
or for when you've got
guests. Use half-fat cream to
keep Points down; it's sold in
aerosols in supermarket
dairy cabinets.

2 sweet dessert apples
150 ml (¼ pint) apple juice
2 trifle sponges
2 tablespoons dry sherry
210 g (7 oz) canned
    blackberries, drained
10 tablespoons half-fat cream
a pinch of ground cinnamon
a few flaked almonds, to
    decorate

1. Core and slice the apples. Poach them very gently in the apple
juice for 2 minutes until softened, but still whole. Drain and reserve
a little of the juice. Let the apple slices cool.
2. Break up the sponges and place in a pretty serving bowl. Sprinkle
with the sherry and the reserved apple juice. Scatter the apple slices
and the blackberries over the sponge.
3. Cover and leave to chill for at least half an hour so the juices
soak into the sponges.
4. Top with the cream and sprinkle with the cinnamon and almond
flakes. Serve immediately.

Per serving: **P 3**
Total per recipe: **P 12**

Ice Cream Sundae

Serves 2

Preparation time: 5 minutes
Calories per serving: 260

Freezing not necessary

Make frozen desserts go
further and look more
attractive with the addition
of some sliced fruits, a
strawberry or raspberry
sauce and crushed ginger
biscuits.

120 g (4 oz) ripe strawberries
    or raspberries
artificial sweetener, to taste
2 teaspoons fresh lemon juice
4 scoops of low-fat frozen
    dessert
1 small ripe banana, sliced
1 ripe kiwi, peeled and sliced
2 ginger nut biscuits, crushed

1. Reserve some of the fruit for decoration. Purée the rest until
smooth and add sweetener and lemon juice to taste.
2. Place the scoops of frozen dessert in two pretty sundae dishes.
Top with the banana and kiwi slices, and trickle over the fruit sauce.
3. Sprinkle the crushed biscuits on top and decorate with the
reserved fruit. Serve immediately.

Variation:
Other fruits can be substituted for the strawberries and raspberries.
Try canned pineapple or apricots in natural juice, or ripe plums,
mango or melon.

Per serving: **P 5½**
Total per recipe: **P 11**